W9-CSI-855

Butterfly Kisses

Poetry For the Many Faces of Love

By

Ebony Farashuu

This book is a work of fiction. Places, events, and situations in this story are purely fictional. Any resemblance to actual persons, living or dead, is coincidental.

ISBN: 1-4033-7787-1 (e-book)
ISBN: 1-4033-7788-X (Paperback)

Library of Congress Control Number: 2002094654

This book is printed on acid free paper.

Printed in the United States of America
Bloomington, IN

1stBooks - rev. 10/03/02

Acknowledgements

I can do all things through CHRIST who strengthens me. Without the power of GOD, none of this would be possible.

Darrell, thank you for being my inspiration, my husband, my lover and my best friend.

Kannon and Darrell III, One day you'll be old enough to read this and know that mommy was one cool chick! You are my sun and my moon and I will forever revolve around you.

Mommy and Daddy, thanks for creating me. (I'll tell you which poems NOT to read.)

Kiona and Diona, you're my favorite little sisters…wait, you're my ONLY little sisters!

Marsha Johnson, thanks for being my "big sister".

Stone Reality, you've been a mentor as well as a friend. I will return the favor by helping the next poet.

Abiodun Oyewole of *The Last Poets*, Thank you for renewing my faith in the power of a love poem.

This book is also dedicated to everyone who ever told me they'd kick my behind if I didn't hurry up and publish my work. Thank you for pushing me towards my dream.

-Ebony-

Dedication:

"Dr." Kym Tunley

You will live forever in our hearts, sweetie. I love and miss you.

CONTENTS

Ebony Farashuu

Farashuu, meaning
BUTTERFLY
Ebony, meaning
BLACK
Ebony Farashuu
I be that black butterfly
Black butterfly am I
And when I verbalize
Or harmonize
My intent is to land on your mind
And leave my essence all over it
Absorb it
Don't try and control it
For it is divinely unexplainable
Physically unattainable
You listen intently to the words I say
At a distance…
For if you reach out to touch me
I'll flutter away
Yes I am that black butterfly
Ebony Farashuu
Black Butterfly am I

BUTTERFLY LOVE

Butterflies are fragile.
Handle with care
For you may damage gossamer wings
Designed to flutter towards love…

Darrell

A ballad with no lyrics is still music…
Sometimes whimsical and wistful…
Sometimes feverish and frenzied…
Sometimes hectic…
Sometimes languorous…
Always music.

I was once music…a staccato tempo with no defined rhythm.
Not always pleasing to my ears and yet…
There was something about my tune
That drew you near.

Joined as one…
YOU sprinkled MY melody with words of love
And WE
Became a song.

Untitled

His name wraps around my tongue
Like a ribbon encircling a shiny new toy on Christmas morning.
His love oozes in and out of my soul through osmosis.
I have absorbed his spirit into the very core of my being.
I want for nothing
I want for nothing
I want for him to never leave me
I want for him to never deceive me
I want for him to make this feeling last forever.
I want for nothing.

Once Upon a Time...

One upon a time...

He's kinda fine
Thugged out
But
Not really...
Black nylon pants, Green Bay starter
Not trying to impress anybody.

Hmmm...

He's kinda fine...
Never really noticed before...
I wonder what he's looking for?
Maybe I can help him find it.

Hmmm...

You say you lost your pager?
No I haven't seen it
But
I can help you look for it.
Ya know, if you want me too...

Hmmm...

I'm in the lead and he's in the rear
And we're walking through this library
Looking for this pager
And we're talking...

5

But
Not
About
The
Pager.

Hmmm…

"Girl you gon' get in trouble…"
He tells me.
"Those caramel legs in that little skirt."

What? This old thing?

And that's how it all began…

Little flirtations
Numbers exchanged at a later date.

Years later I confessed…
"You know… I wasn't really looking for your pager."
He smiled. "That's okay. There never was a pager."

And the story continues…

Look What We Did

Lives intertwined
And we combined
Bringing forth two lives.

Can you believe this?

When we met
I couldn't see our children when I looked into your eyes.
And now...
Eight years later
When I look into your eyes
Our babies are all that I see.

I see Kannon and Tre'
I see you
I see me
I see family

And I think to myself...

Look what we did....

If Only…

If I blinked
My eyelashes would
Flutter against your cheek.

I'm extremely close to you
Yet there are parts of you that
I am unable to touch.

I want to reach inside of your mind
And calm the sea of emotions
Raging in your frontal lobe.

Let me be your escape.
Let me make it go away
If only for a moment.

Come into me and in doing so
Drown yourself in my womanly
Rivers, cleansing yourself of all your troubles.

Let my garden be your haven
Your sustenance
Your source of nourishment
When others leave you hungrily
Searching for a friendship like no other.
I will be the one to envelope you in the folds of my love.

Let me comfort you the way you comfort me…
If only for a moment.

Untitled III

You hold me and the world disappears.
My anxieties
My fears
My tears
Stop
The moment I see your face.
I act nonchalant
When in reality
You haunt my being.
I sometimes find it hard to look at you
For fear I'll become lost
In your eyes.
I don't think you realize
How much you mean to me
For I've only just discovered it
Myself.

Enough

His face was just a shadow in the wan moonlight but I didn't need to
see him,
The sound of his voice was enough.

I had no sweater to protect me from the cold but it didn't matter,
His hand holding mine was enough.

He asked his question. I could not speak.
I answered with a hug instead,
Wrapping my arms around his neck,
Smothering him with my embrace.
He could barely breathe.
He didn't need to inhale air.
My sweet perfume, for the moment, was enough.

I pulled away to smile at the shadowy image before me.
We sat in silence.
There was no need for words.
The comfortable pause was enough.

The odds were against us.
He was a poor man, destined for something greater.
I was his most treasured asset.
To him, that was enough.

There was no ring.
He gave me his word as a symbol of his commitment.
He sealed it with a kiss.
For me, that was enough.

Kissing You

Kissing you is like…
Running through the rain in the middle of September
Arms outstretched
Umbrella sheathed
Moisture dripping through my hair
And seeping through my clothes
Drenching my soul.

Kissing you is like…
Ice cream,
Dripping from a waffle cone,
Sliding through my fingers faster than I can lick
The sweet, sticky flavor from my flesh.

I feel your lips on mine
Before your lips are actually on mine
And I still taste you
Although it's been
Four days since I've kissed you.

Kissing you is like
A poem…
Full of adjectives
And metaphors
Used to make you dig deeper within yourself
And read beyond the words.

It's like that pinch you receive
To let you know that
No, you're not dreaming.
This is real.
These lips, these hands, that tongue
Dance with me

Love me
Kiss me.

Kiss me.

Kiss me.

Because kissing you is like....

Circles

Inspired by the romance of Marcus and Grace Howard

Mesmerized
The mere sight of you causes my breathing to cease.
An apnea in an awakened state
It takes a moment for me to recuperate
For your presence is like a sun shower
Washing over my body and
Rejuvenating my life.

Looking at myself through your eyes
I am vibrant.
Loving myself through your heart
I am strong.
I feel confident and daring
I'm not ashamed of sharing
My love, my body, my soul
With you.

Satisfied
The slightest touch of your hand on my waist
Your fingertips on my face
Stirs within me emotions too sophisticated for written words
Yet too primitive for verbal articulation.
You bring me insurmountable pleasure
Physically
Mentally
Spiritually
This romance is our destiny
Not fully fulfilled.

Ebony Farashuu

All avenues lead to your open arms.
No matter how far I appear to stray
My path is divinely circuitous
For my journey is cosmically fated to begin and end with you.

And as we draw circles in the sky
Connecting our lives
In a sphere of devotion
Our spirits will be linked
Throughout infinity.

Lady Bass

Inspired by Lady Bass, an original painting by Marcus L. Howard of M.G. Murals

My rhythm surrounds me.
And I am the only person in the room as I play,
Lay hands on this bass
As lyrics give chase
To the head bobbin
Line I provide with these
Fingers of mine.

To look at this crowd
Would be like
Coitus interruptus
As the jism does eruptus
So I close my eyes

Caressing and expressing
My love of the music
Like a lover would touch
Her dear heart
I am a part, meaning I am one
With this bass
Can't you tell by my face?

The ecstasy I'm in
As the music literally
Penetrates my skin?

Rhythm surrounds me
As I play…
Lay…
Hands…
On this bass…

15

Ebony Farashuu

BUTTERFLY KISSES

Kiss

A caress with the lips
A gentle touch or contact
An expression of affection

Butterfly

Any numerous,
Slender-bodied Diurnal insects
With broad, often brightly colored wings.
Something that resembles or suggests a butterfly;
Especially a person chiefly occupied with the pursuit of pleasure

Butterfly Kisses

A caress with the lips which leaves your
Mind
Body
and
Soul
Quivering and fluttering like a butterfly drunk from the nectar of love
or lust…

Cyber Sex

His Seductive words caressed my eyes.
I could not hear his voice.
I could not see his face
And yet... I could clearly visualize
The taste of his tongue as he kissed my lips,
The feel of his finger tips as they brushed my hips,
And I shivered.

"I want to taste you", he told me.
I slowly parted my legs,
And allowed my fingers and his words to take me to the edge.
My body quivered.

We're miles apart and yet...
When he tells me that he's holding my hand
My palms begin to sweat.

Is this love? No, it's more like infatuation.
His words pierce my mind like the sweetest penetration.
This faceless man, this soundless voice
Excite me in ways that are so unconventional
But every touch, every kiss, every smile is consensual.
He touches me again.
I flow like a river.

It seems oh so very crazy for me
To be so caught up in this fantasy.
Am I a sinner?
My mind his full of lust for him
My body tingles with passion unfulfilled
In this relationship there is no winner.

I can't touch him. He can't touch me.
But in our imaginations we'll continue to be
Intertwined in that cyber sex dance
Lost in this vortex, this forbidden romance,
Eventually I'll see the error of my ways
I'll wake up to reality and snap out of this daze.
And like the serpent in the garden of my mind
From my life he will sliver.

Can You Feel Me?

Feel that?
Those are my fingernails clawing wildly at your back.
Hear that?
That's my voice calling your name.
I'm not ashamed.

See that?
This is what happens when you touch that spot.
The evidence of my meltdown,
You make me feel so hot.

Taste that?
That's you on my lips and me on yours.
Do you like that? Does it thrill you?
Does it entice, excite, and fulfill you?

I thought it would.
Did you think that it would be this good?

Ooh look at you
Workin' that body the way that you do.
Yeah, keep it right there, that's what I'm talkin' 'bout.
Hit it, work it, make me shout.

Smell that?
That sweaty humidity mingling with your cologne and my perfume?
The musky smell of our oneness is overpowering the room.

Yeah…U like that don't you?
You'll do anything to smell that again, won't you?

Feel that?
That's me shivering against you and you shuddering atop me.
Can U feel me?

All Powerful Woman

You want me.
Don't say it isn't true.
I see the way you look at my lips.
Licking your own as if you were tasting mine.
Wondering what it would be like to sip my wine.

You take a deep breath.
You're trying to keep your cool.
You don't want me to know how my touch thrills you.
But I have eyes.
And your pants don't lie.

You want me.
Don't try and pretend.
Let down your guard.
Let this masquerade end.

Allow yourself the pleasure of my touch.
Give in to the temptation.
Don't use your morals as a crutch.

Let me take you to that place in your mind.
The place that only a woman like me can help you find.
The place that hides your inhibitions.
I want to open that door…I'm on a mission.

I don't close my eyes as I kiss your lips.
I want to see the ecstasy on your face.
I want to see the exact moment in which you lose your resolve.
I want to remember the moment that your freaky side evolved.

I smile as I slide my hand up your thigh.
You gasp as I go higher and I pause.
My fingers are on your zipper.

I'll stop here.
Right before I touch you there.
I just wanted to know.
If I could turn you on.
You didn't think I could
So I had to prove you wrong.
I chuckle as I walk away
Leaving you longing for me in the worst way.
You're a big strong man but your reaction didn't lie.
All-powerful woman, am I.

Ebony Farashuu

Just Imagine

If I penetrate your lips with my tongue
Do you suppose I'd make you cum…
…Pletely lose your mind as my
Fingers travel up your thighs
Would your solder rise
And salute me?
Your commander in chief
Between these here sheets.
Allow this scenario to enter your mind
For one moment just forget about the bump and grind
And instead'
Concentrate on the sweet sticky taste
Of my lips on your lips
No, the ones between my hips
And then the ones on my face
So that I can also partake
In that soul sista flava that you love to saver.
Make haste my brother
This is your only chance you may not get another
Opportunity to experience the vision
That I've so cleverly positioned
In that prison that you call your mind.
Unwind…with me
Let me take you to the top
Or better yet
Let me climb up there
And sit on the tip
Until anticipation has you thrusting your hips
Trying to burrow deeper into that warm place
That I simply refer to as heaven on earth inside of me
Inside of me
Inside of me
Oh, don't you wanna be inside of me.

Is it vivid yet?
That picture that I've painted for you
The canvas is still wet
Better make your move before it dries
And I disappear like the moon on the verge of sunrise.

The Question at Hand

Are you uncomfortable, my Brutha?
Cuz that bulge in your pants has me hornier than a mutha.

Unzip baby, let me help you with that situation.
Let my hands be of service to your mental masturbation.

I want to feel you grow, feel it pulse and expand.
I want to guide you deep into the Promised Land.

I love the way you tremble and shake beneath me.
Your hot, sticky spasms make it hard to unsheathe thee.

Don't want to lose the sensation of you deep inside.
I have yet to be done, I continue to ride.

I dig into your flesh with my knees, you continue to buck.
I continue to moan we continue to fuck.

I won't let you go, I'll keep you within
My hallowed hall of love, until you rise again.

So, once again, I ask, "are you uncomfortable, my Brutha?"
Does my bluntness and honesty make you hornier than a mutha?

A Lady On Your Arm

Is it wrong of me to fantasize?
About tasting my sweetness as it drips
From your talented lips
Once you arise from 'tween my thighs?
Or better yet,

Once you've made it wet
I'll guide you in and let you ride
And once you're done, I'll lick you dry.

The lady on your arm would never attempt
To express these thoughts
Her mind is exempt
From the raunchy words that may be said
By the insatiable whore who inhabits your bed.

You like to be seen with a beauty queen
With painted lips and acrylic tips
A bittersweet voice that would never think to utter
In the language of the prostitute who stands near the gutter
And yet…
We are one and the same.

I Crave You

Long time no touch
Long time no taste
Long time no kisses in that special place.
Long time no hugs
Long time no caress
Long time no hands sliding underneath my dress.
Long time no nibbles
Long time no tweaks.
Long time no attention paid to my mocha peaks.
My hands try and retrace your steps but it's not the same.
When I'm touching myself and calling your name.
I need you.
I want you.
I crave you.

Friction

We toasted with red wine
Now our legs are intertwined
Causing friction
A direct contradiction
To the way this evening was supposed to end
But once I tasted your kiss
I couldn't resist
Wrapping my legs around your waist
And pulling you into my abyss.
Sheer bliss
As we stumble
Tumble
Onto a bed of roses
As the moonlight exposes
Naked flesh
Frolicking in the land of the forbidden
Your serpent
Finds the end of my rainbow
Causing
Friction
Causing
Heat
Causing
Fire

The Perfect Threesome

Secret valleys and low lying crevices
Swell and pulsate with desire
As I caress away the stress of a hectic day
In one shuttering release it's all gone away
It leaves me to wonder
Have I taken things too far?
It's a proven sin and yet I continue
To go back for more until I
Can think of nothing but
Locking myself in a room with my two best friends
Away from this world so full of men
That would do anything for a glimpse into my unknown
Their seeds of curiosity have already been sown
It seems to be
A ménage' trios of sorts
As we quietly disrobe
Teasing each other with unsaid words
Touching each other with steady hands
Giggling as we contemplate
This un-natural love we are about to make
I can't deny
The pleasure that we give each other
The perfect threesome
Me
Myself
I
The perfect one

Pseudonym

You all over me all over you
All over the bed
In a room
Reserved under a pseudonym.

I'm *adickted*
We're both afflicted
With selective amnesia.

I forgot who I was the moment
Your lips
Were all over my lips all over your lips.

I should leave…

The door is so far away
Maybe I'll stay
Long enough for
One more kiss.

I need to leave…

The door is so far away
Maybe I'll stay
Long enough for
One more kiss

I have to leave…

I'm at the door
I can't turn the knob
While you're kissing me and
Oh my god

I'm leaving…

…As soon as the tingling subsides.

So I let my hand slide
Away from the door.
I let my clothes slide
To the floor…

…You all over me all over you.

I close my eyes so I can't see
The essence of WE all over WE
And the sticky guilt all over me.

Lyrical Lovin'

Picked from the brain of Darrell Taylor

Our bodies move to an orchestrated groove
Abstract notes caught in our throats
Sweat mingling, follicles tingling
Toes curling, minds swirling, whirling
In a rhythm unexplained.
Detained, restrained, but never complained
Like a guitar…plucked
Thoroughly fucked, licked, and sucked
Mind blown like Coltrane's saxophone
As our moans
Distinctly
Crescendo

About Last Night

Mind blowin'
Boy, you not knowing
The effects you have on my psyche.

You give me blissful hangovers
My cup runneth over
With this carnal whisky
You're pouring into me

I could smoke an ounce
And still not feel
As high as I do
Right now
At this moment
In this room
On this bed
Trembling
Weak from the aftershocks
Of this intellect altering
Hallucinogenic drug you call
Love
I'll be having flashbacks for the rest of my days
I'll be having flashbacks for the rest of my days
I'll be having flashbacks
For
The
Rest
Of
My
Days
You don't hear me…

VCR

Affectionately known as REWIND

His lips touched my lips touched his lips
touched my neck
touched my neck
touched my neck
I wanted to object
But couldn't get my mind to
Connect
With
My lips
On his lips
On my neck
On my face

Hasty
That's what kind of exit I should have made
But it was just so tasty
My mind was spacey
Tongue-tied in ten knots
As my combative attitude
Raised an invisible white flag.

Captured was I
By his charm
Well aware of his game
But his tactics
Totally disarmed
Me to the point of
Paralysis.

Here comes Dick
See Jane run
Far, far away
And still
I feel
The imprint
Of his kiss
At the base of my throat

If I had a remote
I'd rewind

If I had a remote
I'd rewind
If
I
Had
A
Remote…
I'd rewind
And
Press
Pause.

Watercolors

Deeper than sapphire blue
His voice serenades
Compelling me to rise
Skirt lifted above my thighs
I dance as he watches
He watches as I dance
Lighter than the palest pink am I
As I glide, slide into arms
That hold me like an acoustic guitar.
My love is a taut string waiting to be strummed
As the inner chords of my emotions tremble
With each stroke of his nimble fingers.
Fire engine red, hot lyrics
Rolling from his tongue
Sliding into my ears
Cause my rhythm to quicken
Breathing labored
Our heartbeats synchronize
As sapphire, pink, and red combine
Creating a purple haze.

Mellow Madness

Smooth harmony flirts with my ears and tickles my soul.
Senses overwhelmed, I can do nothing but
Relax
Recline
And let your music slide inside
Intertwine
With my mind
Creating madness too mellow to comprehend
Yet too sensual to ignore
I want to be drenched in your quiet storm.

Gratified

Masturbation
Self Domination
Does it actually bring you pleasure
Or is it
The thought of me
Pleasuring myself
That so
Enthralls you
Who loves to watch
Direct
Inject
Your fantasies
Into my body
As if you were
A syringe?
Understand that I
Will never deny
What gets me through a day filled with
Men who want to fuck me
And women who'd fuck over me
Just to see
The inside of a life
They could never comprehend.
I will never betray me
Never degrade me
And I'll always be there
On the morning after…
So damn it all…
I choose to fall
Prey to myself again and again…
Masturbation
Stress annihilation
Self preservation

Inside

He touched me on the inside part and called my name
He called my name
I can't be blamed for the events
That took place that night.
Call me crazy or
Maybe
A little out of touch
With reality
But when his hand grazed my breast…
It was as if
He reached through my chest
And wrapped his fingers around my heart
He touched a part
Of me
Once cold
Now warm
Ice melting
Dripping
Constricting in his hands.
And while my intent was to
Cease and desist
I could not resist
For my body betrayed my mind
As I was stripped of my clothes
And all common sense
It was intense
The way he
Touched me…
And I was wide open
Secretly hopin'
That this was merely a
Dream or
The result of an overactive imagination

But this copulation was real
And there was something about it that
Appealed
To that little bad girl inside
There was nothing left to hide
I flexed.
He flexed.
We flexed
No longer perplexed
Imagination collided with reality
Was that really me?
Saying those things?
Doing those things?
Wanting
Those things?
He called me my name
I called him his name
And since to myself I refused to assign any blame
Shame
Was
An emotion
That had no bearing on me.
After all, it was *he* that
Beckoned with that
Come- hither stare…
Eyes so black
They seemed to house
The entire universe
For I felt weightless
Every time he looked at me.
Every time he touched me…
On the inside part…
And called my name.

Confessions

When you kiss me…
I feel like…
Dancing naked in the rain.
Sounds insane
Don't it?
But not half as crazy as the pain
I feel
When I watch you walk away
From me
And sometimes
I have to hide with the halls
Of my mind
And reminisce on your tongue frolicking with mine
As you slowly wind and grind against me…
And although we're fully dressed
I can feel how blessed you are
As you pull me closer
Than your shirt against your skin
…feels like sin
And I want to dive in
With you
I want to drown with you.
I want to inhale until my lungs are so full of you
I scream your name with every breath.
I want to confess every time I see your face
But I don't want to interrupt this embrace with
Worthless chatter about my feelings
For they are
Irrelevant.
So…for the hell of it
I keep my eyes closed
And my legs wide open
In anticipation
Of what's yet to CUM.

Untitled IV

My back is against the wall.
Against the wall is my back
My plan was to attack
And then hastily vacate the premises
But his counter attack
Tastily obliterated my defenses
I've lost all sense of time or reason
Committing romantic treason.
And as this situation intensifies
I can't ignore the butterflies
Muttering, fluttering, stuttering
Within a belly that quivers
With pre-orgasmic tremors
As his hands stroke me through clothing
I'm afraid to shed.
My body has been misled
By a mind that promised more abstinence
Than my kitty could deliver.
I shiver
Whenever I imagine him between my thighs…
I want to feel him deep…
I want to keep
A part of him within me forever
And I never want to be without him in my life.
NOW…unrealistic, it may be
I feel things for him that
Should not be allowed to surface.
Yet, I can't disregard the smile
That overtakes my lips when I hear his voice.
His true feelings, I may never know.
My emotions I can't afford to show
For we're both looking out for number one.

Ebony Farashuu

WINGS OF FLIRTATION

Leaving my essence all over you...

Untitled III

Once again
I find myself intrigued by the mere thought of lightly brushing my
lips against yours.
Often discussed but never acted upon feelings of lust
Have no place in our relationship and yet,
I can't help wondering...
Opportunities to be alone together are rare
And when we finally find ourselves in that situation,
The kiss that could have been is replaced with laughter.
The hug that should have been is replaced with a smile.
A silent promise that one-day, things may possibly go further.
But we both know that they won't.
For now I am destined to be with one who does not bear your name.
You are joined with one who does not bear mine.
And so we will continue to flirt without action
Writing hot checks of passion that could never be cashed.
While remaining true friends.

Ebony Farashuu

Coulda

Pimp daddy with no hoes
You've been exposed
Shy guy
Cutie pie guy
You could easily have been
My guy
Well…
If I weren't already taken…
If I didn't love him so…
Boy you just don't know…
These hips…
These lips…
It shan't be said out loud.
Cuz this will never be WE
Just ME who fantasizes
And YOU who feigns shyness
Perhaps I'll write it down
And when I'm as old as you
I'll look upon the folly of my youth and chuckle.
Words written in my mind
In a state of gin induced euphoria.
Shy guy
Cutie pie guy
Coulda been my guy.

Voodoo

Your face appears like a mirage before my thirsty eyes.
My mind is telling me lies.
I stretch like a contented cat,
Satisfied in thoughts of you that
Cause my brain to create fantasies
So delicious I get hunger pangs.
It's a `what if', `could it be' kinda thang.
Could it be?
My thoughts of you
Are actually you
Conjuring thoughts of me?
Throwing off my concentration
With this cosmic penetration?

Stripper Song

Shall I dance for you?
No romance for you
Only what stands before you
What you smell you can't taste
What you see you can't touch
Merely imagine
What it would feel like….
As I slide down this pole
You wish it were your pole
And truth be told
You're the last thing on my mind
As I grind, slow wind, crawl across this floor
Eyes locked with yours
I'm looking right through you
For I see you every night
Same chair, different face
Different age, different race
Whatever…
You all look the same to me…
Green as the cash in your wallet.
No matter how big or small it
Really doesn't matter…
No sex in the Champaign room
No touchy feely
Let's keep it really
I just want to dance
And snatch twenties from your hands.
You only see what you want to see,
Pretty titties, legs up to there
The roundness of my derriere
And all this shiny hair…
But can you see my soul?
When I dance I have control

Of you, of him, of her of them
I'm naked but you're the fool
Putting me through school
And food on my table
When you're not even able to
Kiss me touch me smell me rub me
Throwing money at me that would be better spent at home
On your wife who'd do more than dance for that twenty
She'd do it for free
But I'll never decline when you give it to me.
Just dance harder
Cuz I'm a little smarter
Than the men that walk through that door
And label me a whore
While steadily paying for what they can't have?
Wait a minute…
Doesn't that make him…
MY bitch?

Ebony Farashuu

FLUTTERING EMOTIONS

Confusion
Disillusion
Disenchanted
But love can't be recanted….

Scared

You once asked
What could send me running?
Kiss me

You once kissed me
And I stood still

Still I stood

Wanted to run
But you blocked my path

Scared am I
I am scared

Scared to end it
Scared to continue
Scared to lose you as a friend

Were we ever really friends?
Or were we merely…
Friendly?

Are you really into me?
Or are you trying to get
Into me?

Where is this leading?
I'm blindfolded
Running towards your voice
And away from reality

Once a game

I wonder if I can pull him

Once a game

I'm so shy

Still a game?

I'm laying my cards on the table
I care

How much?
I couldn't say.

Can you?

His And Yours

My heart belongs to another.
What's his is not yours and yet,
I have allowed you to plant your flag deep into my soil
As if I am actually yours to claim.
I am not yours
I am his
And yet
You touch me as if he were never here.
I am not yours
I am his
And yet
You kiss me as if you were the first.
I am not yours
I am his
And yet
He can't touch me
I am not yours
I am his
And yet
He can't kiss me.
I am his
And yet
The arms that hold me are yours.
I am his
And yet
The tongue that waltzes with mine is yours
I am his
And yet
I can feel myself
Slowly
Becoming
Yours.

Delima

I'm drowning in dark pools of chocolate
That used to be eyes
But are now just the vessels used by you
To see through me
My heart
My soul
My emotions are naked behind my mask.
There is no more whiskey in the cosmic flask
Of my denial.
I must go through this trial
With no help,
With no crutch.
I should be alone
Yet I am sinking deeper,
Arms flailing wildly as I begin to lose myself
In the sweet sticky brown that is you
My savior
My wanna be guardian angel
My way out
My hindrance.
YOU who seem to love me
Yet more than content to have me by default.
YOU who must surely lead the league in boards
For you caught me on the
Rebound.
I'm astounded
Dumbfounded
Surrounded in this chocolate pool with no shore in sight
I am unable to tread
And so I sink deeper.
I try to scream
But only manage to fill my mouth
My lungs

My arteries are clogged with your desperate love.
Your reassurances course through my veins like the blood of life
Creating palpitations
Irregularities in a heart that beats for another
Yet, clings to you.
I'm confused.
I could let you go
But then I'd be
Alone.
Which is where I need to be
But somehow
Your arms have become home.
Your kisses, my midnight snack in a cozy kitchen of dreams
Where I am still myself but you are HE.
He that I want
He that I crave
He that visits my closed lids as I sleep
In your arms.
In your bed
In my lies.
And like an alcoholic I drink of you
To ease the pain
Of the loss of him.

Lonliness

Loneliness drapes over me like a mourning veil.
Squeezing me with the intensity of a fierce hug.
Emptiness has hollowed this cadaver that I call my body.
And so…
I fill myself with thoughts of you and memories of times long gone.
And I wait
I wait
I wait
I wait and wait and wait and wait until there's nothing left to do but
stop…
WAITING
Yet love and loyalty keep me here…Hoping…Wishing…Praying.
When in all actuality there's nothing left to do but stop…
Hoping…
Wishing…
Praying…
Waiting.

Us You Me We

What happened to we?
Cuz all I see is me
Reaching out to caress memories
Slowly slipping through the fingers
That once grazed the back of your neck as we kissed...
Damn, I miss the sound of your voice.

What happened to you?
You...who...said you were falling
For me?
You said. So I thought...
But it seems
In actuality
You discovered the edge of my earth
And jumped off.
And though I want to see you
What I really miss
Is the sound of your voice...

What happened to us?
Yeah, when I'm alone
I cry and cuss
And hate you
With unadulterated passion
In this fashion
I try and forget the bliss
Don't wanna reminisce
You make me so sick
And then
I hear
The sound of your voice...

And I have no choice
But to forget the anger of the past
And instead hold fast
Keeping this false security
In my tiny little grasp
Until I choke the situation to death.

Gotta let you go
Gotta free myself
This I know
Gotta deafen my ears
To the sound of your voice.
Gotta stop
Listening
For the sound of your voice.
Gotta stop
Wishing
For the sound of your voice
Gotta stop
Living
To hear your voice…
Don't call.
Whatever you do…don't call…
Cuz I might just fall…again.

Untitled II

Confusion
Disillusion
I don't quite know how to feel
When accosted by emotions so terribly real.
To know you is to love you, To love you is to hate you.
The hardness of my heart you've managed to penetrate through.
I can't deal with the constant barrage of thoughts
Of you that plague me, I'm eternally caught
In a web of despair.
You're in my heart and I wish you weren't there.

Don't Wanna Cry

Day 13
I hadn't cried in days and suddenly…
You crossed my mind.
In that instance
All of my resolved deteriorated.

Tears are gathering in my eyes.
I won't let them fall.
I can't let them fall.

That would only prove
That I haven't gotten over you
Yet…

Deep

Deep inside of me was he
So deep inside of me that he
Somehow managed to fertilize
Once barren ground
Until wildflowers sprouted from my heart
Honeydew dripped from his lips
And coated my hips
In an essence that could only be described as…
Intoxicating
Fornicating
Procreating
He impregnated my soul
Bringing forth
Affectivity
Controlled
By
Objectivity
I had no protection
Against his verbal erection
Tapping on my eardrum
Filling my mind
With meaningless words and metaphors
That sound good in the heat of the night
But leave you lonely
In the cold of the morning after
I was smitten
Bitten
By this vampire who drained me of my
Common sense
And replaced it with blind lust
Confused for love
Abused for love
And my flowers
Became entangled in the weeds I couldn't see
For the blossoms.

Ebony Farashuu

TRIFLING

When you're too pissed off to hide it. Not for sensitive ears.

Why you gotta lie about
Little shit
Silly shit

Lies you spit
Smoother than the legs
You want wrapped around
Your head
Is a little too big
For me.

You want me to believe your love is real
In an attempt to make me reveal
The emotion I feel for you…

Well honey here it is…

I love you hard
My heart is tender
I remember
The first kiss
The first touch
The first time we almost…

Punk
ass
mutha fucka
I thought I was the only one you wanted
For your lover
But you have some other coochie
On reserve
Just in case I won't serve?

Aye Aye Captain Save a
Hold up….

I'm cussin at you
I should be cussin at me
I'm the one who fell for silly lies
I'm the one who fell for deep dark eyes
I'm the one who switched her hips
Just to see you lick your lips
And smile at me
And want me
And now my love for you does taunt me

You ain't worth the tears I cried.
You ain't worth the stress
You ain't worth the split in the dress
I wore just to show you what you'll never have
You ain't worth a glimpse of my pretty little calves

I love you hard
And it's gon' be hard
To get over yo ass
But I will….

Love Is Anger Is Pain

Loving you is like
Torture….
Water
Drip
Drip
Dripping
In a room otherwise filled with silence

I want to scream
When
I hear your voice
But instead I say
"Hey you"
And ask about your day

Never mind the fact that I lay
In bed and pray
For the strength to make it through
Without thoughts of you
To jumble a mind
Already filled
With images
Of days long gone

And I cry
When I'm alone

My tears you will never see
What a fool you've made of me
So in your presence I smile…
I smile
But all the while
I'm dying on the inside

While the outside perpetrates an image of
She who is resilient
While he who killed
The fantasy
Has no clue…
You have no clue what I know about you
You have no clue what I know about you
And some of your lies are so trifling
That I find myself laughing
At shit that ain't even funny
How time flies
When he's having fun at my expense
When he's filling my head with silly nonsense
I tried to go but you needed me to stay
Just a little while longer
I was weak when I should have been
Just a little bit stronger
Hey…
Remember when you were falling in love with me?
Wooing and pursuing me?
Missing me?
Couldn't wait to be kissing me?
Yet you're so easily dismissing me
Like the wet spot in your bed
After you fucked up my head?
I'm so sick of feeling this pain
Drowning in this rain
I'm fucking going insane…
Got you on my brain
And I have no one
To blame
But the foolish woman I was…

UNTITLED POEM

I can't stand
YOU
Make me sick to my stomach
HURTS
When I remember swapping spit with
YOU
Invoke emotions I don't wanna deal with.

Look at me.
Thoughts jumbled
Hate oozing from my pores
Attempting to drown the love
I don't wanna feel.

I don't even like you!
I wanna crush your nuts with the heel of my shoe
You knifed me in
MY HEART
Aches
In memory of the mistake of you.

Damn…

Will I ever be able to shake you?
Forget about how I used to partake of you?
I need to escape from
YOU
Don't deserve the time I wasted.
Wasted like…
Red Kool-Aid at the dinner table.
Get it before it stains the carpet
The way you stained my psyche.
Yes, I invited thee into my world

But your welcome was long ago overstayed.
Played and dismayed, your lies betrayed your true feelings for me
So see…

Love you…I do
Need you…I don't
I won't allow you to purposely victimize me.
That would be like self-genocide
And I refuse to drive my own hearse
So instead I wrote this verse
Which I didn't bother to rehearse
For emotions can't be practiced…
ONLY
FELT

Ebony Farashuu

BUTTERFLY SCENES

The story behind the poem…

Unheard

Unspeakable
Unthinkable
But here I am
Treading water amidst the wave of emotions
That threatens to
Drown me
Every time you come near.
You make me smile when I have nothing to smile about
And for that I
Love is such a strong word.
I like you a lot
And it's not
A crime for me to
Sometimes fancy myself
In your arms late at night
With nothing between us but
The rivulets of sweat
Dripping from your chest and landing
On the sheets
I'm not totally insane
Just a little frazzled
My brain
Sometimes fails to maintain
An adequate balance
Between fantasy and certainty
And therefore
I often feel things that I shouldn't feel
I can't deal with the lunacy of it all
The small things that mean so much
Your voice, your touch, your fingers
Gently playing with my hair
I care waaay too much about you
But every time I try and walk away
I trip and fall
No grace at all
Just a clumsy mess
And I must confess
If only to myself

Ebony Farashuu

I

Love is such a strong word
It should be left unheard
For my own good
It should be left unheard
Even in my own mind
What you don't know won't hurt you
But what you don't say
Could
Scar you for life…

78

Omar undressed quickly, not caring that his linen shirt was being wrinkled or that his slacks had snagged on the chipped corner of my oak hutch. His eyes spoke more than his lips needed. He only cared about what stood before him and as I slowly walked towards him, I only cared about being enveloped in his arms, tightly sealed, and protected from the elements outside of my bedroom. Each time with Omar was better than the last and even if it wasn't, just being held by him, my head on his chest, his calloused hands stroking my hair, lulling me to sleep, more than made up for a couple of missing orgasms.

Omar and I have been seeing each other for about eight months. Actually, it will be eight months this Tuesday. I don't expect him to remember something so insignificant, it's not as if it's been a year but the romantic in me remembers every anniversary, right down to the hour. For instance, He first kissed me on January 1st at midnight. Our third date, this first kiss had been so breathtaking I'd made a New Year's resolution to take things extremely slow with this man. Too often I'd given in too quickly, shown my feelings prematurely and been hurt. This time I'd vowed things would be different.

So far things have been...different. I kept my legs primly closed for six whole months and instead of getting frustrated and threatening to find someone who'd give him what he wanted, Omar seemed content to wait. Of course, I don't put anything past a man but he'd never given me any reason to suspect he was seeing someone else on the side until I decided to give in. In fact, he spent every free moment with me. We even slept in his bed a few times, doing nothing but sleeping. He always stopped when I told him and he never asked why. He simply accepted my word as law, something that both puzzled and intrigued me.

When I finally allowed him to have me, instead of becoming distant, as I heartbreakingly expected, we became closer. Sometimes I feel as if I'll go crazy if I don't speak to him at least once per day, even if it's just to say hello. He makes me smile when smiling is the last thing on my mind. I laugh at his corny jokes with so much honesty you'd think he was performing at a comedy club. He makes me think about things I've never considered in the past. Omar listens to me with such curiosity in his eyes, I know he's absorbing my every word.

Handsome is not a word I'd use to describe him. Omar is...rugged. Skin the color of a semi-sweet chocolate chip, his coarse hair cut close to his head and tapered on the sides, he reminds me of the black man white men fear and envy at the same time. He could easily be mistaken for a quarterback but can out dribble the slickest player on the basketball court at the park near his apartment. He has thug appeal, meaning that he can go from hip-hop to Mozart with the mental agility of an undercover agent. Sophisticated with a streetwise flair, this man has captivated my mind and body in ways I've only read about in books. He is the most beautiful man I've ever met, inside and out.

I like him. Something rare between lovers because once you allow a man to enter your body the next place he penetrates is your heart, usually so suddenly you don't remember falling until he's left you so hurt you feel as if you'll die. That's my theory, which is the reason I've avoided the subject of *love* as if the very word will cause me to whither.

Right now, this relationship feels like a fantasy, a dream I could awaken from at any moment. In past relationships, I've always allowed myself to fall in love with a man without really knowing what he's all about. A few pretty words, some passionate kisses, and a roll in the hay always convince me to give of myself so completely there was hardly anything left for me when he decided he'd had enough.

I tried to walk away from Omar the moment I felt myself caring more than I thought I should but kept tripping and falling over the small things. The way his voice sounds in the morning, the way he kisses me, even before I've brushed my teeth, the text messages he sends me just to let me know he's thinking about me...I don't have the strength to give those things up, but I also don't know if I have the strength to handle the potential breakdown I'd have if he ever broke my heart.

We've never talked about marriage. He's never mentioned where he wants this to go or how he truly feels about me. Of course, neither have I which must shock him because I'm pretty sure he's heard the *"where is this relationship going?"* speech at least twice in his life. I don't want to push him to divulge feelings he'd rather keep secret but I also don't want to divulge my feelings, only to find he does not feel the same.

So instead of saying what's really on my mind, I kiss him softly, snuggle closer, and sleep in his arms, for now pushing all thoughts of *love* far away.

Saturday morning brings with it the sounds I come to adore. Omar trying not to wake me as he slowly slides out of bed, walks into my bathroom and splashes cold water on his face before taking his morning pee, the sound of liquid hitting water as he relieves himself and then washes his hands. I have yet to hear the toilet seat close but I don't care. I'm a big girl. I look before I sit.

"I love you." I whisper to the empty space beside me before sliding out of bed myself, and joining him in the bathroom, kissing him chastely on the lips before sliding into the shower to rinse his essence from my love sore body. He joins me a few minutes later, taking the soap from my hands and lathering up a loofah before scrubbing my back just the way I like.

"What's up for the day?" He asked, writing messages in the soap on my back.

"Hmmm." I answer, trying to figure out what he's written.

"Can't guess?" He asked. I shake my head and he erases what he's written and starts all over again. I say each letter aloud as he writes slowly on my back…

"K-I-S-S-M-E." I smile. "Kiss me." I whisper turning to face him, kissing him on the cheek. "My turn." I take the soap and motion for him to turn around.

"Why is it that no matter who is scrubbing whom, you always end up hogging all the water?" Omar questions jokingly.

"I don't know." I mumble, lathering his back and pausing, finger in midair as I contemplate what to write. I LOVE YOU, I scribble and erased so quickly he barely has time to try and guess.

"What was that?"

"Nothing, let me start over."

"No."

"Okay, then I quit." I attempt to get out of the shower but he grabs me, holding my arms so tightly it almost hurts.

"Misha, why are you acting like this all of a sudden?"

"I'm sorry, I think my period is about to start, I've just been moody."

He gives me one of those "yeah right" looks and I shake my head in dismay, hating his prying eyes. Omar lets go of me and I grab my towel, hastily wrapping it around me, trying to get out of the bathroom before he can ask any more questions.

"Did you write *I love you?*" He asks.

I pause in the doorway with my back facing the shower and imagine his soapy face as he asks the question.

"Why?" I answer.

"I want to know."

"Is that what you wanted me to write?"

"Is that what you wrote?"

"No."

"Okay." He answers simply.

Tears sting my eyes as I walk into my bedroom and stare into my closet without actually seeing my clothes. I love him but I'm so afraid to tell him it's tearing me apart. I continue staring into the closet as I sit on my bed and absently lotion every place I can reach without asking for help. His question rankled me and although it should have been simple to just tell him the truth, experience dictated I keep my feelings to myself, lest I might scare him away from me.

We dressed in silence, he in a pair of jeans he left at my house last week and I in his favorite pair of beige Capri pants. I didn't cook breakfast as I usually did on Saturday morning. Instead, Omar suggested we go to the waffle house for some greasy omelets.

"Who's driving?" I ask.

"I'll drive your car, it needs to be detailed." He holds his hand in the air in anticipation of the keys I'm about to toss him.

Side by side we walk, not apart, but not exactly together as we descend the stairs and head toward the parking lot where his car is parked next to mine. Always a gentleman, Omar opens my door, helping me into the car as if I'm some sort of fragile flower. Then, he does something he's never done before. He leans over me and buckles my seatbelt for me.

"I love you." He whispers the words quickly, as if he's not quite sure how I'll react. The door closes before I can say anything, although, I really don't know what to say anyway.

"Did you say *I love you?*" I ask as he slides in and starts the car.

"Why?" He looks at me with one thick eyebrow raised.

"I want to know." My breathing feels labored and I wonder if he can somehow sense the irregularity of my heartbeat.

"Is that what you wanted me to say?" His question mirrors my own and I look away from him, concentrating on the scenery passing outside my window.

"That's an unfair question."

"It's the same question you asked me." I'm softly reminded. We stop at a traffic light and Omar puts his hand on my cheek. "Hey." He whispers "Can you look at me for a second."

I blink a couple of times to stop the tears that threaten to break through my mental barrier and look at him in what I hope is a nonchalant manner.

"Misha, I love you." He says it again. Slower, clearer so there is no mistaking the words or their meaning. "You don't have to say it back if you're not comfortable with it but, well, I just wanted you to know. I do love you. I have for quite some time. I guess I was just afraid to say it."

He said it. Twice, in one breath. I don't say anything, too shocked to speak, not quite knowing how to respond. In my silence he continues speaking.

"Does it scare you?" He asks. I nod in affirmation and he slips his hand over my hands, clenched in my lap. "Would you like me to refrain from uttering the offensive words?" His tone is so official I can't help but burst out laughing.

"Is that a no?"

"You were right." I say slowly.

"About?"

"About what I wrote on your back in the shower."

"And you lied because?" He probed.

"Because I've been burned by those words too many times in the past."

A car honks behind us, urging Omar to once again out the car in motion. He shakes his head in disbelief.

"So you're grouping me in the same category as a bunch on knuckleheads who probably can't even *spell* the word, much less appreciate what a woman like you has to offer?"

"No."

"Then say it."

"I love you." My voice is hushed as if I'm telling him my darkest secret.

"I can't hear you."

"I love you." I say again, a little louder this time.

"Huh?"

"I love you!" I yell into his ear, laughing despite my reservations of earlier.

"I love you back." He's looking straight ahead, watching traffic but there is no mistaking the smile on his face. I lean back in my seat and intertwine my fingers with his. "So…" He pauses for a moment. "Got anything special planned for Tuesday night?"

"Tuesday?"

"You know, Tuesday? Our eight month anniversary?"

"I'm free." I respond with a smile on my face as well as in my heart. And I truly am…Free.

Aquarium

The cynic within me is screaming for me to hang up but my ego is enjoying the deep octaves of his voice vibrating in my ears as I picture the eyes that held my gaze longer than necessary, the hands that grasped my waist as if he'd already made love to me a thousand times, the lips I wouldn't have minded kissing just once to see if they felt as pretty as they looked. He's asking those *getting to know you* type questions and I probably wouldn't have a problem with it if I actually wanted to get to know him. I'm not looking for love. I'm not looking for a date. Hell, I wasn't even looking for this conversation and I'm still trying to figure out how he ended up on the other side of my telephone line.

We met at a club and when he sent the drink to my table yes, I drank it for I was a bit parched. When he asked me to dance, yes I danced for I needed recreation in order to appease my feet, which had dominance over my mind when the right song filled the room. Justification for my actions are usually easy to come up with but I have yet to explain to myself how my phone number ended up on a cocktail napkin in the pocket of the slacks that hugged his ass just right. Yes, I took a peek as he walked away which was a bit embarrassing because he saw my backward glance as he was glancing backwards at me.

He's too darn perfect and I'm a bit...wary of him. This man is handsome, intelligent, probably has a good job... he's probably married, about to be married, or has a serious girlfriend who doesn't know he was out that night. My mind takes me back to our tango and zeroes in on his hand holding mine as he thanked me for the pleasure, no ring did I spy, no nervous looks around the room, no...particular group of women giving our dance unnecessary attention and quickly dialing on cell phones.

But there *has* to be something wrong with him. There's always *something* wrong with them. Over possessive, dog, lied about having a job, five girlfriends in five different area codes, dog, mama's boy, wheels cost more than his car, crazy and deranged, dog, stalker, looks good but can't put it down in the bed room, big feet with a small wee wee, I mean there is no perfect man. I always seem to attract those ignorant, over possessive, jealous men, who treat me like a possession and fail to realize there is a talented, intelligent woman beneath the MAC makeup and hundred dollar hair extensions. There is pain beneath this happy image of mine and I'm not about to let yet another man add to it. Yeah, there's definitely is something wrong with him, I just haven't figured it out yet.

And I'm still listening, laughing, flirting because despite the fact that I *know* there has to be a major flaw hiding beneath this perfection, he's asking me questions no other man has ever had an interest in having answered.

"You're nosey." I tell him.

"You're intriguing." He counters.

"I'm not going out with you."

"I haven't asked."

This is true. He hasn't asked me out on a date yet. He hasn't asked if he could hit it. He hasn't told me about all the miraculous things he could do to my body. He hasn't really talked about himself at all. He's listening to me. It's almost as if he's really interested in what I have to say.

"Jolie." He pronounces my name the way my mother intended and I instinctively say...

"Yes?"

"Nothing. I just like saying your name, Jolie. Jolie. Jolie. Jolie."

"Solomon." My tone is cautious. "Let's get down to the nitty gritty. What do you want from me?"

"It's not about what I want *from* you. It's all about what I want to do *for* you."

"And that is?" I probe further.

"I want to make your fantasies come true."

"You could never understand my fantasies." Is my haughty response.

"I think I understand more than you give me credit for."

"And I think you underestimate me."

I'm not about to fall into that trap. Tell a man your fantasy and he'll pull it off so perfectly you'll be dropping your panties so fast you can't remember whether you were even wearing them at the beginning of the date. Why should I tell him what's in my heart? That would only give him the fuel he needs to set his plan in motion.

"Fine. Don't tell me your fantasy. Don't tell me what you expect from a man and don't lump me in the same category as the fools in your past." His chastisement leaves me uneasy.

"Fools?"

"They had to be. You're not with them."

"You want to know my fantasy?"

"Only if you want to tell me."

"And if I don't want to tell you?"

"I'll make up my own and hope that you'll follow along."

This makes me smile, makes me slightly drop my guard but I'm not going to make this easy for him. I'm not going to tell him exactly what I want. Instead, I recite a poem, which has been in my heart for years. I've had it on my mind for so long, if it were a piece of paper it would be weathered, worn and unreadable.

Iridescent
Blue
Illuminates you
Illuminates me
Illuminates us
As we
Dance
I'm entranced
With my reflection
In your eyes
And as I inch closer
To get a better look
Your lips brush mine
Ever so lightly
And as I inch closer
To get a better look
You hands grasp mine
Ever so tightly
And the room begins to glow
Iridescent
Blue.

"That's my fantasy." I say casually.

"That's easy." He replies.

"Oh yeah? What are you going to do? Put a blue light bulb in a lamp and hope your kisses turn me on enough to get me into your bedroom?"

"You've been hurt." His reply is simple and to the point.

"I've been *educated*." I correct him. "You'll never get close enough to hurt me."

"Then I'll never get close enough to love you. I'll never get close enough to find out if you're even a woman I could *see* myself falling in love with. I'll never get to know you, Jolie. No man will. You have to let go of what *they* did. You say you've been educated but you failed to learn that shielding your heart isn't going to keep you from getting hurt."

Another layer of steel begins to slide away from the invisible wall I've built around myself and fear grips my heart as my hand grips the phone a little tighter. The realization if how desperately I want him to surpass my expectations has totally weakened what little defense I had left.

"May I try?" He asks softly. "I'll only ask once and if you never want to hear from me again I will delete your number from my memory."

Okay. I'm hooked but does he have what it takes to reel me in?

Ebony Farashuu

Part II: The Fantasy

The silk scarf fits snugly over my eyes and as the road bumps slightly beneath the floorboards of his car, I can hear the sounds of traffic passing by my window. Unable to see, I must rely on my senses in order to try and figure out what Solomon has in store for me. Unafraid, unashamed, I am curious to know what it is about this man that has had me on edge for days. I can't see him but his very presence overwhelms me to the point of dizziness. His cologne, not too strong, mixes and mingles with my perfume, creating a scent that is one part Solomon, one part Jolie, totally one with each other and I know I never want to wash my sweater because this new and exciting scent has probably been absorbed into the fibers. Dionne Farris plays softly throughout the car and I can relate to her feeling of hopelessness for I felt hopeless the moment I answered my front door and saw Solomon standing there holding that black silk scarf in his hands. He was dressed comfortably in jeans and every now and then I would hear his hand or something rub up against them briefly as he drove. Were his hands sweating the way mine were?

I shifted in my seat, self consciously pulling at the tan, silk skirt I was wearing, hoping I wasn't showing too much leg because although I couldn't see him, I could feel Solomon looking a me. For the hundredth time, I asked where we were going. For the hundredth time he answered,

"Just ride, Jolie. Just ride."

So I rode as he drove. He drove as I rode beside him, silently, wanting to lift the scarf a bit, just to see the scenery passing by, but refraining because I don't want to ruin his attempt at making my greatest fantasy come true. Could he possibly understand how much that poem meant to me? Could he possibly comprehend the meaning behind the words? The car slows to a stop and as he gets out, I wait silently, anticipating what lies ahead.

"We're here."

He opens my door and helps me out, being careful to shield my head from the roof of his car as I gingerly place my sandals on ground that feels hard, like pavement. We're walking now and his hand holds mine firmly, leading me into nowhere for I hear no other footsteps besides his shiny shoes and my low-heeled sandals echoing through what I presume to be a parking lot. He knocks three times on a door that sounds metal. I reach out to touch it as we walk through and I am pleased to feel cold steel beneath my fingertips.

"What are you smiling at?"

"Was I smiling?" I chuckle.

"You have a nice smile."

"I hope I'm still smiling when you take this blindfold off." I sniff the air, "It kinda smells like fish, where are we, near the river?"

He doesn't answer, merely stands behind me, puts hid hands around my waist, and gently pushes me forward. He tells me that he has to leave me for a moment and walks away, leaving me standing blindly in the middle of a hollow space. Things are going bump and I strain my ears to try and figure out what's going on around me. I lift my hands to my face, just about to yank the blindfold off when I hear soft music begin to play.

"Don't trust me?" He's standing in front of me. My hands leave the scarf and reach out for him, needing to feel him to be sure he's really with me. "Close your eyes."

"Closed."

He gently removes the scarf and puts his arms around me, slowly grooving to the music playing in the background.

"May I open my eyes now?" I ask.

"Not yet, pretty."

"Pretty?"

"Yeah, Jolie. French for pretty."

"You're pretty clever."

'I try."

"So can I open my eyes?"

"Can you just dance with me and forget about where we are for one moment?"

"No offense, but I've been blindfolded for almost an hour."

He chuckles softly, "Okay pretty, open up."

I slowly open my eyes and realize I can barely see his face in the iridescent blue light of the room. We're both bathed in the blue light coming from the wall before us but it's not really a wall. It's a thick paned glass and behind this glass are the most magnificent sharks I've ever seen, swimming around, occasionally bumping the glass.

"The aquarium." I gasp, not even attempting to hide the delight in my voice.

I glance up at him, smiling like a kid with cotton candy all over her face.

"How did you?"

"Your poem."

"But how did you get this out of my poem?"

"Remember when we were talking about our favorite TV shows?"

"I remember."

"And you said you loved to watch any show about Giant Squids or sharks."

"You were really listening…" I whisper softly. "I mean, you not only listened…you *heard* what I was saying."

"Isn't that what I was supposed to do?"

Despite earlier anxieties, I take a small step closer, bridging the tiny gap between our bodies, filling that space with flesh against flesh. Solomon holds me close as I fight the urge to lay my head on his shoulder and inhale his dizzying cent until my knees become weaker than they already are. I keep my eyes open, watching the sharks swimming around, loving the way the soft blue light really does seem to make us glow and I lift my gaze to meet his, looking him directly in the eye, smiling at my reflection. Is he inching closer or it that me leaning upwards as he leans downward, softly brushing lips as if we're both trying to see where this dance is headed?

"Can I hear it again?" He kisses my forehead as he makes his request and I'm so entranced with the moment I almost don't hear him.

"Hear what?"

"I want to hear about the iridescent blue…." He chuckles.

And I begin to speak delicately, my voice barely above a whisper but my mouth is near his ear so I know he hears every word.

"Iridescent
Blue
Illuminates you
Illuminates me
Illuminates us
As we
Dance
I'm entranced
With my reflection
In your eyes
And as I inch closer
To get a better look
Your lips brush mine
Ever so lightly
And as I inch closer-"

I don't finish. His mouth is on mine before I can get the rest of the poem out and all I can do is close my eyes and ingest the sheer flavor of his soft lips. As we're kissing we begin to move until we are almost leaning against the glass of the aquarium and the sharks must be wondering what the hell we're doing and this has to be the most surreal experience I've ever had in my life. I'm running out of breath just thinking about taking things further than I should. I want to break this contact before it goes any further but I don't want him to stop kissing me because it feels so good. I take a deep breath and slowly begin to drag my lips away from his.

"Are you hungry?" Solomon asks

"I'm starving.' I tell him. "But can we stay here a little while longer. I just want to watch them swim for a while."

His answer is a smile. He drapes his arm around my shoulder and we begin to discuss where we're going to eat and what we may possibly want to do when we hook up tomorrow and as we chat, the music slowly fades, the sharks keep swimming, and the room continues to glow iridescent blue.

-The End-

Familiar Stranger

I didn't know him from Malik
But from the way
His cheeks exposed cavernous dimples
Every time our gazes connected
I knew his name could easily have been
"MY"
Last name "MAN"
Hyphenated "FOREVER"
His shiny bald head reflected the disco lights,
Blinking messages in Morse code
And I wanted to send up smoke signals in response.
I was ready to show and tell this man my
Every secret
Providing answers to questions
That had yet to form in his mind
We were two people in a crowded room
But all others were transparent
For my eyes saw only him
Walking towards me
Smiling,
Hands outstretched in a silent invitation to dance.
Ghetto beats faded as we slowly swayed amongst frantically moving
bodies
That gyrated to a groove
Unheard by our prejudiced ears.
Mental segregation separated us from the masses
And we must have looked divinely strange
Slow dancing while Tupac commanded everyone to
Holla if you heard him.
I didn't care
His nose was in my hair
His hand on the small of my back
Never attempted to southerly stray
But instead, guided me through the crowd
To a place that granted us privacy unimagined in our minds.
"I knew you in another life" he told me. "You were a black orchid
and I was a Monarch butterfly hungrily feeding upon your sweet
nectar."

Ebony Farashuu

"Is that why I always felt so drained?" I asked.
Past lives and reincarnations aside
He slid his hand over mine
And whispered things to me I'd only seen on paper
And I, in turn, read him my diary from memory.
I want a man like this, I need a man like that,
Don't hurt me, desert me, and overexert me to the point of exhaustion
From chasing this pipe dream.
"Stop running" he told me.
"What?"
"Stop running. Stand still and let me come to you, for I've heard you
in my mind...wandering around, not trusting me to find you on my
own. What you sought stands before you and what you seek you've
already found."
So I stopped running
And stood still
Staring destiny in the eye...
And offered my heart to a familiar stranger.

Normally an awkward situation, I feel no embarrassment by the fact that I've been caught staring the man across the room. Surely he had to be gazing at me in order for our eyes to have met in such a prophetic fashion. His dimpled assessment of my outward appearance assured me his eyes approved of the modest yet form fitting top I've paired with jeans tight enough to tantalize yet loose enough to discreetly store a little pocket change.

I look away, merely out of necessity. My throat is parched, dryer than stale birthday cake and I must drink at least half of my self-purchased Long Island tea. I say, "self purchased" loosely because it's not as if I haven't had my share of offers. I mean, I've turned down at least five brothers who have that bill-of- sale look about them. You know what the bill-of-sale look is... It's when a brotha buys you a drink and then decides that he's just put a down payment on the rest of the night. It's a damn shame what some fools expect for the price of a five dollar cocktail. No cocks in _this_ tail please, I must graciously decline your offer of refreshment but you have a good night brotha. Keep steppin'.

98

But anyway, as I finish my drink and turn back to the specimen at hand, I can do nothing but inhale at the sight of him. He's so fine it almost hurts my feelings. Because men like this are usually found only in fantasies and there is nothing worse than waking up to find it's all been a figment of your imagination. I blink, just to be sure that REM is not to blame for the vision before me. He smiles again and in an instant I know that this man must belong to me. I see his smile and raise him an eyebrow, for all bets are on the table now.

Disco lights bounce across his chocolate baldhead as if he is speaking through Morse code but I don't have time to interpret the message. He's walking towards me. His approach is almost dream like, as he appears to float through the crowd with a ghost like quality. He holds out his hand and I grasp it not knowing or caring where this man is leading me.

The rhythm is slow and sensual as he places his hand on the small of my back, holding me close, as love songs seem to play for us alone. His touch is intriguingly familiar and as he buries his face in my freshly washed hair, I lay my head on his linen shoulder and once again I inhale. With my eyes closed and senses wide open, I know I've smelled this man before. I've felt his caress and tasted his sweat as it slides from his forehead to his nose and drips from his lips as he makes love. In my heart, I have known this man and in the same heart I've never met him, or have I?

Did the song change or are these other people on the dance floor out of place? Because this slow groove I'm swaying to doesn't mesh with the corybantic gyrations of the couple dancing next to us.

"Let's find a quiet place." He tells me.

I have yet to speak to him and it takes a brief moment for me to realize that this is the first time I've heard his voice since we touched.

"I know you." I whisper. "But how?"

"I suckled your nectar in another lifetime."

"You were a butterfly."

"And you were a black orchid."

Mutual recognition seals our fate and as I walk away with this familiar stranger, I will learn that his name is Donovan Trent. I like to think of him as "My Man Forever."

-The End-

Photo Credit:
Photographed by Don Crane of Don's Photography Studio
Tulsa, OK

Hair:
Rashida Riggins
Masters of Hair II
Tulsa, OK

Cover art designed by Darrell R. Taylor Jr.

About the Author

Ebony Farashuu is from Tulsa, Oklahoma. As a spoken word poet, she has touched the eyes, ears, and hearts of all who have been exposed to her uniquely sensual and emotion provoking style of poetry. Like a butterfly to the sweet nectar of an African violet, Ebony Farashuu's poetry provides mental nourishment for lovers, those who want to be loved, and those who have lost love. Ebony is currently wrapping up her first full-length novel.

Printed in the United States
26915LVS00001B/406-426

9 781403 377883